Knowing Your Worth

By Towanna Odom

Knowing Your Worth
©2022 by Towanna Odom

ISBN: 978-0-578-29674-6

Printed in the United States of America
Library of Congress Cataloging -in- Publication Data

Book Cover Design by: Taminko J. Kelley of CoolBird Publishing House
Published by: CoolBird Publishing House

Table of Contents

Disclaimer:

This book is fiction and was written to bring consciousness to real life situations one may be facing.

Psalms 37:4

"Delight yourself in the Lord and he will give you the desires of your heart.

Chapter 1

Who Am I?

I'm living in a big dream doing big things, walking with my nose and head in the air, living in my big house, wearing fancy clothes, driving my expensive car, and knowing just what to say. I have it all- I'm always doing it all.

My life is picture prefect in the eyes of the world, but inside I am an emotional mess. How can I have it all and feel so deeply lost on the inside? What must I do to match my soul to the outer part of me?

Feeling up and down sometimes, feeling like I am on a merry- go- round waiting for it to stop. Each time it goes around, it seems to never end. I'm tired. Tired of waiting for it to end. I'm feeling dizzy and drained.

I'm up all-night crying with my mind filled with deep thoughts of worry, stress, and pain-feeling like my head is about to burst. My heart beats with anxiety from the hurt and trials I've endured, every beat feels like the last beat, every breath feels like the last breath.

As the anxiety gets stronger the tears get longer. I'm screaming, "God, PLEASE TAKE THIS PAIN AND TELL ME WHAT TO DO!" Things are silent, no one is speaking and there is no direction of what to do. If I take myself out people will have so much to say. If I check into a hospital, they will think I'm crazy.

Rehabs are too expensive and what can they tell me? They're having problems and issues too. I have no help and I don't know what to do. I picked up the strong pills and decided that I would sleep through the pain. Day after day, night after night as the pain gets more intense, the pain pills become stronger.

Finally feeling like I have numbed the pain, I am high as a bird that's flying way in the sky and numbing myself has made my days go by. Behind my pain there is a story to tell but being on pills have me not able to think clear or speak well.

Looking in the sky wondering to myself, "Who am I?", "Who have I created myself to be?" and "What is the name that the streets have chosen for me?" I'm a pill popper and I take any kind of pills. I think I can manage, but they are really getting the best of me, I use them to sleep, but it's getting harder for me to think. Selfishly knowing that it's hurting me and the people that are a part of me.

Working hard for money to give to the pill man is my truth. People are preaching to me telling me not to do it, but I'm not listening, at this point, I barely know my name. I do not need help; I can shake this habit at any time. It's not an addiction, it's my own convictions. People need to leave me alone because we have all done wrong.

I am human and the mistakes I made is my reality that others have also experienced. My friends are using pills and I am not as bad as them. I can control my life; pills will never get the best of me. I'm trying to convince myself that I'm not an addict while telling my story has made my nightmare become my reality.

Looking at this piece of my so-called life, I drive my fancy car barely paying the note. I have the clothes that are so nice, my outer appearance is looking good, but my inside is like muddy water with piled trash. Trash that needs to be cleaned and taken away. I have no money and I borrow money before I get paid. My heart constantly speaks to my mind. I tell myself that I am so tired of my demons chasing me. It has made people not want to be around me. God, please deliver me!

Devil, get up off me!

Deliver me from my demons, and my bad habits that are getting the best of me. How can I become a pill popper trying to hide the feelings that are inside? The scars and the wounds are getting deeper. Pills, problems, depression, and secretive lies are all growing inside of me like the limbs on a blossoming tree waiting for me to break free.

I prayed and asked God to get the devil off me. He showed me that my biggest enemy is inside of me. I did not trust Him enough to pray for myself and give my problems over to Him. I tried to fix myself and I became so mean. I felt like a ticking time machine.

I am going to start speaking life into myself and waiting on the spirit of God to finish the work that He has begun. I believe in my heart that it can be done. If He spared my life, He could also save my life from the enemy that does not want me to live.

I once heard a preacher tell me that there were levels and steps that I needed to take to be free. Time after time I came into God's presence thinking that I was not worthy of being free from all that I had done to myself and others. One day I made up my mind and I decided to take the steps that the preacher spoke about.

Step 1- I accepted myself and that I had an issue that I couldn't control on my own.

9

Step 2 - Realizing Philippians 4:13 I can do all things through Christ that strengthen me.

Step 3 - Getting myself help by checking into drug rehabilitation and making up my mind to get the help that I needed.

After getting clean, I needed strength to get through the hard times. I said and wrote the scripture Philippians 4:13, "I can do all things through Christ that strengthens me." daily around my house. I learned it and I felt it. I said each word slowly until it pierced my heart and my soul.

Anytime my addiction tried to get the best of me, that scripture gave me strength to know God gave me the power to overcome my addiction and any other obstacles in my life. Some days were harder than the others, but with the help of the Lord, I was able to make it each day. Every time I looked in the mirror, I was so impressed to see the person that I had become. I am healthy, happy, and finally free.

If you are this person and you know you need help. Please don't wait until tomorrow to get help. Tomorrow is not promised to you. You owe it to yourself to be FREE. There are many rehabs that offer free services, so do it...Release the demons, let God arrive, and the drug demons will be scattered!!!

Chapter 2

Self-Love

The look you give me, the way you make me feel and the sweet things you whisper into my ears. Grabbing my attention with the love you are showing, you have me feeling like I have always wanted to feel. The attention I receive has me wanting to believe every word you say knowing that things you do are not okay.

I have given my love to my partner, and we have become one. The things I feel sometimes are not real. I have placed my heart in the middle of a broken field. I will stick with it because someday things will change. I know you love me because I am told everyday regardless of how you never come home and always stay away. I am willing to stick things out.

I'd rather be with someone I know than be alone. You will change someday because I believe in you. You tell me you are sorry, and you never mean to treat me that way. The verbal abuse, lies, and cheating is something all couples experience. I do not know how to love myself because my love for you is so strong. What people don't see is the way you make me feel behind closed doors...they are judging you and not giving you a chance

I am willing to forget myself and make things right just for you. I know that everything I do is worth the fight. Take my mind and my soul- you can have total control. Just tell me what you want me to do. I am willing to do anything because I am so in love with you. I'll go to work. You never have to work as long as you treat me like you love me. I will be that person that will always love and believe in you.

All the wrong things you do, I will forever close my eyes to. You take my car leave me in the house until it's time for work. You say you're out handling business and never come back in time. How could I be so stupid to still ignore the signs? Your phone is locked, and it rings all night long. I have invested so much time into you.

I will never let another person win. I'm hoping and praying our relationship will have a better end. I put you before myself, my kids, and my family too. I'm living in your shadow because you know just what to say to make me stay. How could I be so blind to constantly walk around feeling this way?

I take up for you when people say bad things about you. You make sweet love to me and make me believe you are the one God has for me. You tell me, "If I leave, I will forever regret I did.

I laugh at every word that you say knowing that in the back of my mind that it's not okay. You're only saying those words to me to make me stay. The words you say have me feeling like your love for me is so strong and that really turns me on. You tell me, "Baby I hit you because I love you".

I could leave and give someone else my attention, but I know you are the one for me. I will do whatever it takes so that we are together as one. I grabbed my pillow and smiled. It feels like you are confusing your love to me. I keep giving you a second chance because your second chance will never end. People say to love myself and I really want to but the love I have for him feels so true! I am denying the insecurities that they tell me I have.

Do they think relationships are peaches and cream every day? The people who speak on my relationship are miserable and do not have a relationship.

They judge me because they are jealous. They say my relationship has brought me too much pain. That is totally insane. I'm in love and this is how it goes. You help your partner to be better, you stay there through thick and thin and that is how you both win. I WILL BE HERE UNTIL THE END.

Years has passed and my life is slipping away but I'm trying to stay. We argued because I didn't answer my phone. I tried to tell him that I left my phone at home. The words that I said did not pierce his ears. He pulled out his pistol and shot me in the face. There he stood looking at me as if he had lost control. As I laid in my puddle of blood, I prayed, "Lord please don't let me die, please HELP ME, and show me the way. I promise to get out of this relationship if you give me a second chance."

While praying, I seen the angels of the Lord appear before my eyes. That's when he ran out of the door to get away. I mustered up enough strength to reach for the phone to call the police. I was able to get help and to live another day. I had to undergo many surgeries just to bring me back.

I spent months trying to recover from it all. I promised myself I would never get into another relationship that would have me feeling this way. Being single gets lonely sometimes but being honest with myself and recognizing when a relationship is getting the best of me is more important.

Knowing how to love yourself is POWERFUL. Love is strong and it can have an everlasting bond.

It shows empathy and you will know when you meet the right person. That person will always be in your corner and will always have your back. Happiness is the key to any relationship. If there is more hurt and pain in your relationship than happiness, then please be reminded of your worth and know that loving yourself is more valuable than loving someone that does not love you the way you desire.

When you love yourself, no one will treat you less than how you want to be treated. A toxic, abusive relationship with a man or women will make you lose control of who you are. Know your worth and know that SELF LOVE AND RESPECT IS IMPORTANT. There are so many people that are murdered daily from domestic violence. Get out while you can. All lives matter!

Chapter 3

Depression

Look into my eyes, tell me what you see.
Depression has taken over me. I rush to my bed
after work every day feeling like there is where I
want to stay. Anything someone says makes me
want to cry.

I have no pleasure in any activities and I'm always
sad. This has become my mood with the people that
want to see what is wrong with me.

Shhh... it's this thing called life that is getting the
best of me. Bills, children, relationships, sickness,
finances and so many other challenging things that I
face. I know I've been overwhelmed, but I can't
figure out why I'm feeling this way. I have
problems and I was taught to speak life into myself.
I will not let the devil play with my mind this way.

As I look in the mirror, I want to find happiness, but
I only see that I have gained weight excessively. I
have gained weight from laying in the bed doing

16

nothing but sleeping and eating. I walked out of the mirror not liking what I had seen, I picked up TD Jakes' book. I wanted to read it, but I couldn't concentrate nor read. What's wrong with me?

Everything I feel? My children know something is wrong. How can I continue to raise them if I'm not acting and thinking on my own? My children are sad and really feel alone. They are ashamed because I fuss in front of their friends, and I am not engaged in their lives like I need to be. The school is needing more money from me than I have, and their friend's parents are doing for them what I need to be doing. I'm living in the dark looking like a bad parent. How do I tell them that their mom is losing control of her life and don't know what to do?

One day I laid in my bed and a commercial glorified my ears. It said depression is real and if I took one pill a day of Citalopram I would be healed. I sat in my bed thinking this could be a sign from heaven for me. I decided to secretly get help so that I could help my family. I no longer wanted others to take care of my children each day. I went to a doctor, and I was told that I was depressed. I said, "Doctor, I totally agree. Please help me, my problems seem to be getting the best of me."

I took his advice and started the medication. It seemed to be helping. I was getting better and was starting to feel like I was becoming free. Depression no longer had control of me. I got out of bed and was happy at work. I was no longer that angry person I once was. With counseling, medication, and God's help I was back to being me. Some may say no to counseling, and say that alcohol has been the trick for them...

If we look around, mental illness is running rapid. It has caused some to give up and commit suicide. Some have lost their mind, and some have even had nervous breakdowns. There are many walking around not knowing who they are. Counseling and sometimes medication is a way of releasing life issues and helping us. God gives us wisdom and knowledge, and He also gives doctors the wisdom and knowledge to help us. With God's help and a doctor to assist, anything is possible. Depression has been a major problem in so many households, mainly in children. In this world we live in today, social media has bullied so many children. It has also applied peer pressure to make them feel like they must do anything to go viral.

If you are experiencing any of these issues, please do not ignore the signs and seek help. Parents, do a wellness check on your children daily and watch for signs of depression. Don't allow them to lock themselves in their rooms and you do not know what they are doing or how they are feeling.

If I can help one person daily to overcome depression, that one person may be able to help another person. We could break strongholds of depression all over the world. One mind, one body and one soul.

Don't destroy yourself by thinking help is not for you.

Break Free!

Chapter 4

I Need a Man

I need a man; I need a man. I am as thirsty as I can be. I need any man just to look at me. I don't care what he looks like as long as he gives me the attention I need. I will give him what he wants as well as what he needs.

There is a shortage on men, and I am tired of being without someone to call my own. He can be big or tall, I am so desperate I will take them all. I need a man so bad; I am losing my integrity. I want someone to put out the trash, mow the lawn, hold me, and comfort me. As time passes by, I am wondering did God forget about me. Men today play a bunch of games and dating is totally not the same. Men are not interested in knowing your name, they only want to see women undress and you know the rest. God knows that my dating life is a mess.

Men now are only interested in the women with long hair, a thick butt, and a slim waist. And let's not forget the ones who had surgery in their butts and face. How can I compare to those bodies? They're everywhere! Social media has made dating become very hard. Women are always showing all their body parts. I cover up trying not to show nothing at all and men never look my way.

Whatever happened to men falling in love with women with natural beauty and brains? Why aren't people dating and learning one another's name? What happened to genuine love that never fades away? What happened to the men that always opened doors? What happened to the men that had respect for women? What happened to the women that respected themselves? What happened to the women that never wanted to go under the knife? What happened to the women that were not looking for a man only for financial gain? Love is not the same!

I wonder if I will ever get married, or will I die alone? Lord, please help me and tell me what I'm doing wrong. I see some women that are as happy as can be and they've had multiple marriages! I am begging God to give one good marriage to me.

I spoke to an older gentleman, hoping he could help me understand what was I doing wrong. He said, "A woman needs to understand that a man like me with financial stability is looking for a woman that thinks like me. I want her to have goals that she can bring to life and a woman that I can count on to be my wife. I will be her backbone and she would never feel alone. If she wants a real man like me, she will know her worth enough to wait on marriage and not rush me. I need God to show me if she would be the right person for me. Waiting on God will bless her with a man as fine as me." I was thinking, "Is he speaking directly to me?" "I don't care for the fake bodies, long lashes and hair hanging down their back. I want a real woman that uses her natural nails to scratch my back."

I listened to each word that hit my ears and thought, "This is the type of man I have prayed about for years". I was super excited about the words that were spoken to me. His words helped me to wait on God to bless me with the man that I deserved. I pictured myself walking down the aisle marrying the man of my dreams. From that day forward I promised myself that I would not accept anything less than what God has for me. I know God will not forget about me because He loves me.

Women, never sell yourself short just to feel loved. Take back YOUR CONFIDENCE and wait until the right person comes your way. You will never be blessed with the right person until you remove the no-good mess. Get a man that acts and thinks like he is GROWN and always remember that all grown men have their own.

Chapter 5

Grief

How could you leave me when I wanted you to stay? How can I go on each day? I never thought my life could go on without you. I was not ready for your sudden death, but God saw that you leaving me was fit.

The pain, the dreams, nightmare, and scares are all hard and running so deep. It feels like someone has torn my heart into multiple pieces. I try not to question God, but how could He call you home so fast? I don't think this feeling will ever pass. I often think of the times we shared- the laugher, love and so much more. It seems like I can still smell your scent at the door.

I wish this feeling was a dream that would end in a better way. I never wanted you to leave, come back please! My mind is in bad shape mentally and emotionally. I'm feeling like I will eventually have a nervous breakdown. You were one that I will always think of and adore. I know that God does not put no more on us than we can bare. I am feeling like this pain has overwhelmed me. I am not strong enough for the task He has placed upon me.

Each day I pray for myself to have the strength that I need. The burdens of you leaving me will never end. I feel myself getting strong enough to face each day. I will live with the past that we once shared. Healing is a process, and I am scared. Scared of what's next on my journey without you. Watch over me while you are away. I will do what I need to survive while I am alive. We shared a bond that will always live. Even though you are gone, you will always be in my heart.

Death is hard for some to believe, but we all will have to leave. We all have a birth date and a death date, and all deaths will not be the same. Grief is something we all must experience. The passing of loved ones is hard, and no one ever wants to experience the pain of it. Many people have passed from grief and disbelief of their love's one's death.

If you are grieving and it has become uncontrollable, please seek help. There are people that are in place to help you get through it. There are no words that can make you feel the way you need to feel, but prayer, counseling and surrounding yourself with people that love you can help you heal. Every day will not be a good day, but with the

strength of the Lord, you will see yourself
becoming stronger.

Psalm 34:18

The Lord is near to the brokenhearted and saves the
crushed in spirit.

Psalms 73:26
My flesh and my heart fail: but God
is the strength of my heart, and my portion forever.

Matthew 5:4

Blessed are they that mourn: for they shall be
comforted.

Chapter 6

Trapped

Who am I? Why am I the person that has been hiding me? Why do I have to live a life secretly? People say my life is a sin, but I was born this way. Why can't I be accepted like others and people have nothing to say? They say that same sex is a sin, but the bible says all sex without marriage is a sin.

I am not accepted by my family because they say God does not honor me being gay. The church has cast me aside because they say I am not right in the eyes of God. If God does not make any mistakes, how could He create me this way?

Some may say they were born this way; others say they were forced to have this desire from tragic things that has happened to them. But if God loves everyone, why am I not good enough for Him.

I pray to God each day and I try my best to obey. I try to live up to the expectations of how others feel my life is supposed to go. Lord why don't they know? Please help them to see I am as human as I can be.

When a woman loves a woman, she is painted as normal. Women are painted as bicurious and I am painted as being nasty. I am looked upon as a great disaster to my family. I want to live my life in the open, but it has caused me so much pain.

I am thinking of changing my name. Maybe if I leave and change my name they will not complain. I then thought of something that would make me look the same. I married a woman that showed interest in me. She had doubts in her head that I was not wholehearted. She thought she could change me. Our lives were picture perfect in the eyes of people. I married and gave it a try. I wanted to be the man that they said God created in me.

I closed my eyes and did it the right way and we became one sexually. There I laid not wanting what I just had and immediately I became sad. As time went on, we developed a child that touched my soul. I then felt a little complete. I had the family that I needed but the desire of me wanting to be free from the person that was inside of me was worrying me. I wanted to come out desperately.

I stepped out to do secret things with men and I felt like it was okay. Deep down inside I think she already knew. It wasn't hard for her to see that my friends were as feminine as could be. I was living a double life and was hurting someone that really loves me.

God, free me from me! I prayed every day for God to show me the way. I prayed, "Take this feeling away from me Jesus! JESUS I AM YOUR SON, HELP ME!" I prayed and prayed. One day God began to show me that I was living a life to please people. He showed me that I had to put Him first so that He could take control.

What He had to do for me was to free me from me. This time I was serious as I could be because I was tired of living a double life. It was taking a lot out of me. I went before God, and I admitted to Him that I no longer wanted to be trapped in a lifestyle that was full of lies. I no longer wanted to have an eye for the same sex. God showed me that my life was not a mistake and He needed to do a work in me. He loves me as His son, and He said I still had a chance.

We all have come short of His Glory. He explained to me that any person not living in His Will, will not live. The person I am did not embarrass God because He loves me. Sex without marriage, and adultery both are a sin with anyone not only the same sex, but anyone who is having sexual engagements while not being married will not make it into the kingdom.

Once God helped me to see me, my own convictions held me accountable for me. God showed me how to fall in love with my wife so that we could have a sincere life. He took my desire for the same sex away and healed me. My wife forgave me for living a secret life and she still wanted to be married to me.

You may think God can't change your life, but He can. You can do things a certain way for many years but when God does a great work in you, the things that you once desired will no longer exist. You can be FREE. Some may not want to change, and some may want to change. The way to change is to seek God constantly. Hiding your life from people will never help you to be free. It will only have you trapped in a place of no return.

Never marry to try and prove to others that you are the way they want you to be. Live, learn and grow into the place that God has for you. Give God room to do a work in you and BE FREE. You may lose a lot of friends along the way, but God's peace will comfort you.

Chapter 7

Anger

Ephesians 4:26, "Be ye angry, and sin not: let not the sun go down upon your wrath." Those words would never sink through my ears. Get out of my face, don't touch, or talk to me! I am frustrated, angry and as unhappy as I can be! Everything people say or do are making me feel like they are not for me. I have been feeling attacked. This world really does not understand me. I don't care about how anyone else feels because I am only looking out for me.

I am not afraid to die nor am I scared to take a life. Blood for blood tear for tear. Who cares how I seem or appear? Some may say I have a cold heart others may say I don't care. What can you say, you were not there? Where was your God when I almost died when those traps were prepared for me that I couldn't see? Who was there to care for me?

The streets have made me to realize nobody loves me. I have experienced so much growing up. I had to survive on my own. Most of my childhood I didn't have because I had to be grown. Nobody looked after me. My mom was addicted to drugs and my dad disowned me. The streets taught me all that I know- killing and stealing was the best way to go.

I need my money right now; I don't have time for a job. I don't think I'll live that long. I carry a gun and I'm not afraid of jail. The devil showed me that I already have my ticket to hell. I was always told I would never amount to anything, and I have lived up to their expectations and views. I get it how I live because I grew up on the rough side of town.

No one respects each other and we must do all that we know to survive and stay alive. They said I would be dead or in jail before I turned 15. There's no hope for me, can't you see? The devil has hardened my heart and his blood is all over me! Acting out of anger I did something that landed me before the judge. He told me I had 10 years to start but I wasn't afraid I didn't have a heart.

While doing my time I watched my cell mate pray for me. I told him I did not believe. He said God would change me. I looked at him and turned my head. I knew what he said was dead, but he prayed anyway. My heart became weaker in a way I couldn't explain. The next day I started listening to what he had to say. He told me that God could change me to be the man I needed to be. I said God would never love a man who has dirty hands like me.

He said open your heart and watch Him work on you. I opened my heart and tears fell before my face. I knew something had taken place. I learned that God had more in store for me. As the years went by, I became a changed man. I had a relationship with a man whose face I'd never seen- but I felt Him in my soul. I had no doubt that He was in control. The ticket I had for hell was voided. My ticket is now going to a different place all because my past had all been erased! So many spoke a curse over my life with the negative words they had to say.

We need to watch what we say about the children of our future. Don't count them out. Sometimes, the people in the street make it hard to love them, but God has changed some of our lives and our wrong doings. It is not too late for God to help them as well. I challenge you to try and help one person that you see in life who is headed in a different direction. We do not need to lose our next generation to the streets. Black lives should matter to blacks too and with your help, our generation will win.

Chapter 8

Family

My friend's family is as happy as can be. I wish I had a better family to share that same love with me. If I had a good family, I would cherish every moment with them. I never want to speak to my family again. They are low down, dirty and is never there! They never seem to support my dreams and never seem to care. They sit around spreading gossip and lies. I try my best to stay away from those guys.

Sometimes, I wonder why God placed me in a family like this. If I died, I probably wouldn't be missed. My family only wants me around to help supply their needs. How can I supply all their needs when I need someone to help me? People say that the one's kin to you are the worst. Those words seem to be my family's truth.

I often dream of my family having reunions where we can laugh, eat, talk, and play at a nice venue, but that will never be my family because they would fuss, fight, and argue. My family has a generational curse of pain that need to be cut off at the root! That's the only way we will see each other's point of view. We need to heal from past hurt and pain. This family has driven me insane! God, please see my family through. Our grandparents did not teach us to be like this.

A sudden death in the family came our way, so we had to come together anyway. This funeral will be a start. Funerals bring families together in grief. They see family members that they haven't seen in a while, and they greet each other with a big smile. After the funeral, they promise one another that they will do better and keep in touch. A month later they're nowhere to be found and things are back to the same way until something happens again.

A family will never win acting this way. Family should be loving and supporting of one another even when it's not easy to do. Family should be one that will bend over backwards for you. No matter what a family goes through, the love should never fade away. Families should check on each other from day to day.

Never hold on to family disappointments for the rest of your life. People are dying every 60 seconds. Holding on to things will only leave you with regrets of what could and should have been done after it's too late. I will continue to trust God that we will get better with one another. I will not give up on my family because it is worth the fight. I will be the bigger person and the glue to keep us together. We asked God to fight the battles for us because we couldn't do it alone. The power of God is over my family so strong. I prayed for them and was waiting for an answer from God. He gave me a word that my family has won AGAIN!

Never give up on your family. Some families may have things that need to be ironed out and some families may be on one accord. If we took the time to understand and listen to one another and be slow to judge the other person, so many families could win. Psalm 133:1, "How good and pleasant it is when God's people live together in unity." I challenge you to not be the problem of your family and be the voice of reason so your family will win.

Chapter 9

Manifestation Time

You may sit in a place and feel like there is nothing for you to do, but God will allow you to manifest anything you put your heart and mind to. Many have watched others take off with their dreams wishing it was them and some may say they want to do so much in life, but don't know where to start and that it all seems so hard. But what if I start my vision and it doesn't go as planned?

Everything we do will not go as planned and that is why we pray and ask God to hold our hand- Hold our hand as we step out on faith. Every disappointment we come across is worth another fight. When things go wrong never let your mind go with the things. Thinking you will lose can have you confused, and you will never begin.

A positive mindset brings positive things and positive always win! If you are feeling like you want to write, pick up a pen and begin. Pray and ask God to lead the way because He encouraged me to say what you are reading today. I know if He did it for me, He can do it for you. It's our winning season that we are walking into! We are walking by faith and not by sight! We are all running the race and the growth starts within.

Changing your mind frame is how you win. I challenge you to start writing your vision down and to begin working on it. Let it manifest this year! Don't go into another month or year sitting on your dreams and goals.

It's manifestation time, YOU WILL WIN!

Chapter 10

Prayer

Dear Heavenly Father,

As we come to you, we ask that you forgive us of our sins. Lord, we confess the Lord Jesus with our mouth and believe in our hearts that you raised him from the dead. Right now, Lord Jesus we ask that you come into our households. Do a new thing in us so that we can do great works for you.

Lord, I pray for my sisters and brothers that may be facing anything out of either of these chapters that you have allowed me to write. Father God, I ask that they be healed, delivered and set free from bondage in any way. Lord, rebuild and strengthen the areas that they may have been torn and broken. Lord, I ask that you rebuild and when you rebuild, please don't allow them to make the same mistakes over again.

Help the people on the streets that will not let go of their ways... that drug addict, that alcoholic and so many more. Lord, help us to put you first and not the desires of this world or the things that we want to fulfill our flesh. Help us to walk away from all strongholds and release your great works into the world that you are doing in us.

Help us to help others come closer to you and help us not to judge one another as you manifest your work in us. Father, we thank you for speaking to us and guiding us. We thank you for allowing us a second chance to get it right as well as help someone else along the way. Father, I ask that you give the
resources that they need to go forward in their dreams, visions, and goals.

I ask that you make us the head and not the tail, the lender and not the borrower, above and not beneath. Father, as we seal this prayer, we want to tell you thank you for all you have done and is about to do in our lives and the lives to come.

Father, we thank you and give you all the glory in your son Jesus name,

Amen.

About the Author

Towanna Odom loves the Lord and serves faithfully in the Church of God in Christ. Towanna studied Business, she is a native of Jackson, Mississippi and currently resides in Atlanta, Georgia. She is a proud mother and a grandmother.

Her mission is to help others overcome life issues and show them that they do not have to stay in a sunken place in their lives. She believes that if she helps one person overcome life challenges, that one person could help the next person and then this world could be a better place.

Her mission is to also teach people how to love themselves enough to trust God to lead them out of darkness. She loves traveling, shopping, praying, encouraging, and uplifting others. Her favorite bible verse is Psalms 37:4, "Delight yourself in the Lord and he will give you the desires of your heart.

Made in the USA
Columbia, SC
18 May 2023

16884630R00024